ESSENTIA

Air Freshener
Room Spray Recipes

by Kathrine Townsend

CLADD
PUBLISHING

Cladd Publishing Inc.
USA

This publication is designed to provide accurate information regarding the
subject matter covered. It is sold with the understanding that neither the
author nor the publisher is providing medical, legal or other professional
advice or services. Always seek advice from a competent professional
before using any of the information in this book. The author and the
publisher specifically disclaim any liability that is incurred from the use or
application of the contents of this book.

Essential Oils Air Freshener: Room Spray Recipes

ISBN 978-1-946881-53-3 (e-book)
ISBN 978-1-946881-52-6 (paperback)

Contents

Benefits of Essential Oils

Instead of avoiding air freshers altogether, you can easily create non-toxic and natural room sprays yourself. Plus, essential oils do more than just make your home smell nice; they offer antiviral, antifungal and even antibiotic properties.

Essential oils aid in the prevention and cure of colds, reduce stress, eliminate odors, alleviate headaches, and create an inviting and luxurious atmosphere.

Commonly Asked Questions

Q: CAN I DO THESE RECIPES WITH LITTLE EXPERIENCE AND ON A BUDGET?

A: Yes, while the recipes are based on luxurious products they are budget friendly, non-toxic formulas. This is an excellent book for the average person wanting to enhance their life with high priced essential oil products; but do not want to purchase the expensive version from a specialty store.

Q: WHAT DOES EO MEAN?

A: EO or EOs is the abbreviation for Essential Oils. It is commonly used and will be used in this book.

Q: CAN I SUBSTITUTE ESSENTIAL OILS?

A: You can swap out oils or substitute for your favorite in almost all cases. However, do not use citrus essential oils for products you intend to wear directly in the sun.

Q: GLASS BOTTLE OR PLASTIC?

A: Essential oils can degrade plastic. That is why its recommended to store oils in glass.

Q: BASE PRODUCT VS. CARRIER OIL?

A: A base product is a cream, lotion, shampoo, gel or anything that has already been made. You can add a few drops of essential oils to enhance the product. A carrier oil is a pure oil, that is used to dilute the strength of EOs, and help prolong its aroma.

As a rule of thumb, I wouldn't apply essential oils directly onto your skin without diluting it in a carrier oil first. Although, there are some that you can do this with, unless you are experienced avoid direct application.

Q: CAN I ADJUST THE STRENGTH OF THE RECIPE?

A: Yes, you can and should limit the drops of essential oils based on your personal sensitivity towards the strength. Most recipes in this book are medium strength. However, you can always reduce or increase slightly in either direction unless stated.

FRAGRANCE OIL VS. PURE 100% ESSENTIAL OIL

A: 100% pure essential oils are required for these incredible recipes. Do not purchase "fragrance oil" or "perfume oil" as these can be synthetic and don't provide the desired health benefits. Instead, look for oils that say, "pure essential oil" or "100% essential oil" for the highest quality.

Essential oils come from plants, while fragrance oils are usually artificially created and will contain synthetic chemicals. Even though they smell similar and cost less, they do not provide the same therapeutic benefits.

Q: RAW, ORGANIC AND NATURAL

A: For the highest quality ingredients use raw and or cold pressed honey, coconut, shea butter, aloe vera, jojoba, beeswax, cocoa, and sweet almond oil. Try your best to obtain supplies that are organic and or natural.

Essential Oil Uses

ANTIBACTERIAL:

- Bergamot
- Clove
- Cypress
- Eucalyptus
- Lavender
- Lemon
- Lime
- Marjoram
- Melaleuca
- Oregano
- Patchouli
- Peppermint
- Roman Chamomile
- Rosemary
- Sage
- Sandalwood
- Wild Orange
- Wintergreen

ANTIVIRAL:

- Cinnamon
- Clove
- Eucalyptus
- Lavender
- Lemon
- Melaleuca
- Oregano
- Sandalwood
- Thyme

ANTIFUNGAL:

- Eucalyptus
- Lavender
- Lemon
- Melaleuca
- Patchouli
- Sage
- Sandalwood
- Thyme

Any combination of these essential oils can help purify the air in your home. With so many ways to use essential oils to clean your indoor air, they're easier to use than you think! And once you replace artificial scents with natural ones, you'll never want to go back.

The Miracles of Lavender

Lavender has been used for medicinal and home care purposes for thousands of years. It is by far the most versatile EOs you can get.

COMMONLY USED FOR:

- Skin rashes
- Acne
- Insect bites
- Minor burns
- Soothing agent
- Relaxation
- Odor eliminator
- Disinfectant

A few drops of Lavender EO in a bath will soothe nerves and aid you in sleeping. It can be rubbed into your temples and forehead to relieve headaches with a carrier oil. In addition, a sachet of Lavender EO can keep moths away.

It's fantastic to use as odor control for laundry, stinky socks and sweaty gym clothes. Add Lavender EO to a mop bucket to super clean your floors

Tea Tree "The Medicine Cabinet

Tea Tree is often called "the medicine cabinet in a bottle," as it can be used to treat almost any common ailment.

You can add a few drops of it to unscented shampoo to alleviate dandruff, psoriasis, and head lice.

COMMONLY USED FOR:

- Athlete's foot
- Dermatitis/eczema
- Acne
- Cold sores
- Nail fungus
- Warts
- Insect bites
- Disinfectant
- Bug repellant

Lemon's Versatility

This is the most versatile EO out there. It can be used for everything imaginable, and is very safe to use and ingest in the kitchen. I include Lemon EO in many of my everyday uses, foods, cleaners, therapeutics and medicine.

COMMONLY USED FOR:

- Relieves bad breath
- Lessons dandruff
- Alleviates anxiety
- anti-microbial sanitizer
- Disinfectant cleaning agent
- Odor eliminator
- Lemon substitute for cooking

Perfect Peppermint

Peppermint is much like lemon when it comes to the vast uses for this amazing EO.

COMMONLY USED FOR:

- Alleviates nausea and an upset stomach
- Relieve stomach cramps and queasiness
- Draws out insect
- Relieve bronchial congestion
- Soothing
- Eliminate odors
- Antibacterial
- Deter rodents and spiders: they can't stand the scent of it

Eucalyptus Alleviator

Eucalyptus comes from Australia, and is one of the few Essential Oils that you should always have on hand.

COMMONLY USED FOR:

- Alleviating chest congestion
- Eases asthma attacks
- Lessens the pain of fibromyalgia
- Reduces pain associated with the shingles speed the healing process
- Eliminate germs and odors
- Disinfectant

Numbing Powers of Clove

Clove EO has been used for dental issues for ever. It is considered one of the best treatments available for toothaches, gum disease, cold sores, and canker sores. It should always be diluted, and used with caution on very- sensitive skin.

COMMONLY USED FOR:
- Athlete's foot
- Prickly heat rash
- Wounds and cuts
- Fungal infections
- Insect bites or stings
- Bruises

- Ear aches (poured on a cotton swab and tucked just inside the ear canal)
- Repels Mosquitos, moths and fleas
- Odor remover

Calming Chamomile

Chamomile EO has been used to sooth and calm since the Roman era.

COMMONLY USED FOR:

- Boils
- Dry skin
- Eczema
- Dermatitis
- Acne
- Bee and wasp stings
- Cuts
- Bruises
- Soothing

- Relaxes
- Aids in sleep
- Stress, anxiety, depression reducer
- Eases PMS and menopause symptoms
- Repels mites and fleas

Frankincense

Frankincense has long been considered one of the most valuable Essential Oils of All time.

COMMONLY USED FOR:
- Acne
- Warts
- Cuts and scrapes (it's a great disinfectant)
- Boils
- Scar tissue
- Cysts
- Insect bites
- Alleviates stress, anxiety, panic attacks
- Aids in sleeping, depression and insomnia
- Reduces headaches, migraines

Grapefruit

COMMONLY USED FOR:

- Swollen lymph nodes
- Oily skin and hair
- Cellulite
- Acne
- Migraines or tension headaches
- Deodorant
- Repels fleas
- Anti-bacterial
- Odor eliminator

Oregano

Oregano EO is anti-inflammatory, anti-fungal, anti-parasitic, anti-microbial, and antiseptic. It is great to use around the house and on your body. However, never use undiluted. The undiluted oil can cause skin irritation, so wear gloves if you're going to use it full strength for home cleaning purposes.

COMMONLY USED FOR:
- Fungal infections
- Bruises
- Athlete's foot
- Sprains

- Arthritis pain
- Fibromyalgia
- Tendonitis
- Cysts
- Warts
- Candida
- Shingles
- Herpes
- Anti-bacterial
- Repels bugs, mites, lice and fleas

Aphrodisiacs Oils

The following essential oils are excellent options to use as sensual room spray aromas.

YLANG YLANG

Ylang Ylang has a powerful floral aroma, and is an aphrodisiac. Has a feminine aroma.

NEROLI

Neroli has a sweet floral aroma, which is very soothing to an overworked nervous system. Has a feminine aroma.

Rose Absolute Bulgarian

This is a highly-prized EO and is one of the best aphrodisiacs. Rose has a deep floral aroma and is symbolic for the expression of love. *Has a feminine aroma.*

Jasmine Absolute

Jasmine is an incredible aphrodisiac and sexual tonic. It is very calming to the mind and nervous system. It has deep, warm, floral notes. *Has a feminine aroma.*

Sandalwood Australian

This has woody, balsamic, and earthy tones. Its aroma is valued for its ability to calm the mind. It is also used as a sexual tonic. *Has a masculine aroma.*

Patchouli

It is well-known for its aphrodisiac properties. Patchouli is very grounding and intoxicating to the senses. Has a masculine aroma.

Vetiver

This warm, smoky, woody EO is very relaxing. It gently sedates an overworked mind. Has a masculine aroma.

Easy Mix Yourself Instructions

This air freshener recipe is a safe and aromatic way to freshen up the air in your home or work space, without the toxins. If you have a favorite Essential Oil blend, then just add it to this basic recipe for a wonderful room spray.

Ingredients

- 1 ½ - 2 cups distilled water
- 1 tablespoon baking soda
- 5 to 6 drops of your favorite essential oil

Instructions

In a small bowl, stir together the baking soda and essential oils. Transfer the baking soda to a spray bottle and then fill the remainder of the spray bottle with water. Shake until the baking soda has dissolved.

Use the air freshener in all rooms of your house or office.

Air Freshener Recipes

Sweet Lavender Air Freshener

Ingredients:

- 3/4 cup water
- 2 tablespoons vodka, rubbing alcohol, or real vanilla extract
- 8 drops lavender EO
- 6 drops chamomile EO

Use:

- Add all ingredients to a small spritzer
- Shake well
- Spray in the air or on any surface

Eucalyptus Dream

Ingredients:

- Add 5 drops bergamot EO
- 2 drop eucalyptus EO
- 2 drops lemon EO
- 1 cup distilled water

Use:

- Add all ingredients to a small spritzer
- Shake well
- Spray in the air or on any surface

Orange Bliss

Ingredients:
- 4 drops orange EO
- 3 drops cinnamon EO
- 1 cup distilled water

Use:
- Add all ingredients to a small spritzer
- Shake well
- Spray in the air or on any surface

Aphrodisiac Aroma

Ingredients:

- 5 drops chamomile EO
- 2 drops orange EO
- 3 drops ylang ylang EO
- 1 cup distilled water

Use:

- Add all ingredients to a small spritzer
- Shake well
- Spray in the air or on any surface

Divine Sensation

Ingredients:

- 1 Tbsp. witch hazel or cheap vodka
- 13 drops bergamot EO
- 6 drops cedarwood EO
- 6 drops orange EO
- 1 cup water
- 1.5 tsp. baking soda
- 8 oz. spray bottle
- Pour the alcohol into the bottle
- Add the essential oils and gently swirl
- Add the baking soda
- fill the rest of the bottle with purified water
- Gently shake until the baking soda has dissolved

Use:

- Add all ingredients to a small spritzer
- Shake well
- Spray in the air or on any surface

Cool Breeze

Ingredients:

- Add 13 drops spearmint EO
- 13 drops tangerine EO
- 9 drops bergamot EO
- In an 8-oz. spray bottle
- Fill spray bottle 3/4 full of distilled water
- fill the rest of the way with witch hazel

Use:

- Add all ingredients to a small spritzer
- Shake well
- Spray in the air or on any surface

Fresh Squeezed Lemonade

Ingredients:

- Add 30 drops lemon EO
- 5 drops basil EO
- 5 drops spearmint EO
- In an 8-oz. spray bottle
- Fill spray bottle 3/4 full of distilled water
- fill the rest of the way with witch hazel

Use:

- Add all ingredients to a small spritzer
- Shake well
- Spray in the air or on any surface

Pink Sunset

Ingredients:

- Add 13 drops ylang ylang EO
- 12 drops sweet-wild orange EO
- 11 drops sandalwood EO
- 4 drops patchouli EO
- In an 8-oz. spray bottle
- Fill spray bottle 3/4 full of distilled water
- fill the rest of the way with witch hazel

Use:

- Add all ingredients to a small spritzer
- Shake well
- Spray in the air or on any surface

Summer Morning

Ingredients:

- Add 13 drops tangerine EO
- 11 drops lavender EO
- 5 drops lime EO
- 5 drops spearmint EO
- In an 8-oz. spray bottle
- Fill spray bottle 3/4 full of distilled water
- fill the rest of the way with witch hazel

Use:

- Add all ingredients to a small spritzer
- Shake well
- Spray in the air or on any surface

Fresh Herbs

Ingredients:

- Add 18 drops lemon EO
- 9 drops rosemary EO
- 7 drops thyme EO
- 7 drops spearmint EO
- In an 8-oz. spray bottle
- Fill spray bottle 3/4 full of distilled water
- fill the rest of the way with witch hazel

Use:

- Add all ingredients to a small spritzer
- Shake well
- Spray in the air or on any surface

Hawaiian Vacation

Ingredients:

- 19 drops sweet-wild orange EO
- 11 drops ginger EO
- 10 drops ylang ylang EO
- In an 8-oz. spray bottle
- Fill spray bottle 3/4 full of distilled water
- fill the rest of the way with witch hazel

Use:

- Add all ingredients to a small spritzer
- Shake well
- Spray in the air or on any surface

Holiday Room Spray

These Essential Oils sprays smell wonderful, and aid your immune system in fighting seasonal colds.

Apple Pie

Ingredients:

- 16 oz. spray bottle
- 8 oz. distilled water
- 2 oz. Witch Hazel
- 18 drops orange EO
- 10 drops cinnamon EO
- 10 drops ginger EO

Use:

- Add all ingredients to a small spritzer
- Shake well
- Spray in the air or on any surface

By the Fire

Ingredients:

- 16 oz. spray bottle
- 8 oz. distilled water
- 2 oz. witch hazel
- 12 drops douglas fir EO
- 13 drops cassia EO
- 14 drops orange EO
- 4 drops clove EO

Use:

- Add all ingredients to a small spritzer
- Shake well
- Spray in the air or on any surface

Chai Wonderland

Ingredients:

- 16 oz. spray bottle
- 8 oz. distilled water
- 2 oz. witch hazel
- 20 drops orange EO
- 5 drops nutmeg EO
- 5 drops cinnamon EO
- 4 drops clove EO
- 5 drops cardamom EO

Use:

- Add all ingredients to a small spritzer
- Shake well
- Spray in the air or on any surface

Frosty Morning

Ingredients:

- 16 oz. spray bottle
- 8 oz. distilled water
- 2 oz. witch hazel
- 23 drops peppermint EO
- 23 drops orange EO

Use:

- Add all ingredients to a small spritzer
- Shake well
- Spray in the air or on any surface

Gingerbread Man

Ingredients:

- 16 oz. spray bottle
- 8 oz. distilled water
- 2 oz. witch hazel
- 18 drops ginger EO
- 8 drops cinnamon EO
- 8 drops clove EO
- 4 drops nutmeg EO

Use:

- Add all ingredients to a small spritzer
- Shake well
- Spray in the air or on any surface

Perfect Peppermint

Ingredients:
- 16 oz. spray bottle
- 8 oz. distilled water
- 2 oz. witch hazel
- 27 drops peppermint EO
- 18 drops ylang ylang EO

Use:
- Add all ingredients to a small spritzer
- Shake well
- Spray in the air or on any surface

Spice & Everything Nice

Ingredients:

- 16 oz. spray bottle
- 8 oz. distilled water
- 2 oz. witch hazel
- 18 drops bergamot EO
- 8 drops ginger EO
- 8 drops cassia EO
- 7 drops white fir EO

Use:

- Add all ingredients to a small spritzer
- Shake well
- Spray in the air or on any surface

Trim the Tree

Ingredients:

- 16 oz. spray bottle
- 8 oz. distilled water
- 2 oz. witch hazel
- 12 drops cinnamon EO
- 11 drops orange EO
- 18 drops white fir EO

Use:

- Add all ingredients to a small spritzer
- Shake well
- Spray in the air or on any surface

Zesty Gathering

Ingredients:

- 16 oz. spray bottle
- 8 oz. distilled water
- 2 oz. witch hazel
- 17 drops orange EO
- 8 drops clove EO
- 8 drops rosemary EO

Use:

- Add all ingredients to a small spritzer
- Shake well
- Spray in the air or on any surface

Linen Spray Recipes

Fresh Linen

Ingredients:

- 1/4 cup distilled water
- 3 tablespoons witch hazel or vodka
- 20 drops lavender EO
- 15 drops frankincense EO

Use:

- Add all ingredients to a small spritzer
- Shake well
- Spray on sheets, pillowcases, and linens

Happy Life

Ingredients:

- 1 oz. water
- 1 oz. witch hazel
- 3 drops eucalyptus EO
- 3 drops lemon EO
- 2 drops tea tree EO
- 2 drops peppermint EO

Use:

- Add all ingredients to a small spritzer
- Shake well
- Spray on sheets, pillowcases, and linens

At the Party Recipes

Mojito Madness

Ingredients:
- Add 11 drops lime EO
- 10 drops grapefruit EO
- 11 drops tangerine EO
- 10 drops spearmint EO
- In an 8-oz. spray bottle
- Fill spray bottle 3/4 full of distilled water
- fill the rest of the way with witch hazel

Use:
- Add all ingredients to a small spritzer
- Shake well
- Spray in the air or on any surface

Rid Smoke Odor Recipes

Smell Eliminator

If you smoke or live next to someone who does, you can easily eliminate the smell of cigarette smoke with a few drops of essential oils.

How To:

- Add four drops of rosemary EO
- 3 drops tea tree EO
- 4 drops eucalyptus EOs
- Place in an 8 oz. spray bottle
- Fill to the top with water
- Shake well
- Spray anywhere you can smell smoke odor

Stress Relief Recipes

Blooming Garden

Ingredients:
- 4 drops lavender EO
- 3 drops rose EO
- 2 drops clary sage EO
- 1 cup distilled water

Use:
- Add all ingredients to a small spritzer
- Shake well
- Spray in the air or on any surface

Life Is Easy

Ingredients:
- Add 14 drops grapefruit EO
- 14 drops sweet-wild orange EO
- 6 drops lemon EO
- 6 drops bergamot EO
- In an 8-oz. spray bottle
- Fill spray bottle 3/4 full of distilled water
- fill the rest of the way with witch hazel

Use:
- Add all ingredients to a small spritzer
- Shake well
- Spray in the air or on any surface

Sleeping Aid

Restful Night

Ingredients:

- 5 drops lavender EO
- 4 drops chamomile EO
- 1 cup distilled water

Use:

- Add all ingredients to a small spritzer
- Shake well
- Spray in the air or on any surface

Relax in the Meadows

Ingredients:

- Add 13 drops lavender EO
- 13 drops cedarwood EO
- 13 drops spruce EO
- In an 8-oz. spray bottle
- Fill spray bottle 3/4 full of distilled water
- fill the rest of the way with witch hazel

Use:

- Add all ingredients to a small spritzer
- Shake well
- Spray in the air or on any surface

Printed in Great Britain
by Amazon